CONTENTS

978-1-898015-16-1

Published by *Fur and Feather*
for
Coney Publications
Chattisham, Ipswich, Suffolk IP8 3QE
Telephone: 01473 652789
www.furandfeather.co.uk

"I became interested in rabbit nutrition when I first started work as a nutritional advisor over 10 years ago. Whilst I was advising owners on the correct diet to feed their dogs and cats I realised that many of my rabbits' problems were diet related. My first rabbit 'Clover' was fed bowls of brightly coloured dry food and I am now horrified to admit that we filled the bowl right to the top. My second rabbit 'Smirnoff' frequently suffered from sticky bottom and more worryingly succumbed to fly strike one summer. She survived but the maggots ate a huge chunk of flesh from her rump and I will never forget how gruesome the sight was. Sadly, the vets never suggested a change in diet for Smirnoff and I carried on cleaning her bottom for many years. Once her diet was altered I saw a remarkable change. She was fed on fresh grass, vegetables, hay, water and just a few grams of a higher fibre, single pelleted rabbit food. She no longer suffered from sticky bottom, the fur around her genitals grew back, the raw skin healed and she slimmed down nicely."

Fiona Campbell

The digestive system of the rabbit

It is important to know how the digestive system of a rabbit functions if we are to understand why an incorrect diet causes so many health problems.

The rabbit has a very complex digestive system. They are herbivores (plant eaters) and their digestive system is more similar to a horse than that of a dog or a cat. They are hind-gut fermenters, meaning that most of their food is digested in the large intestine (specifically the organs known as the cecum and the colon).

Fibre is an essential component of the rabbit's diet. A rabbit needs to eat both digestible and indigestible fibre for health. Indigestible fibre is vital to maintain gut motility (keep food moving through the digestive system) rather than as a source of nutrients. The digestive system should always be moving and a lack of indigestible fibre can cause serious health problems including gastrointestinal stasis. A diet high in indigestible fibre has also been shown to prevent fur chewing in rabbits.

Diets which contain high levels of digestible fibre are crucial to encourage the growth of normal intestinal flora (also known as friendly bacteria). A lack of fibre (and a diet too high in protein and carbohydrates) may result in dysbiosis, which is an overgrowth of the harmful bacteria (including *E.Coli* and *Chlostridia*). Dysbiosis often causes diarrhoea in rabbits.

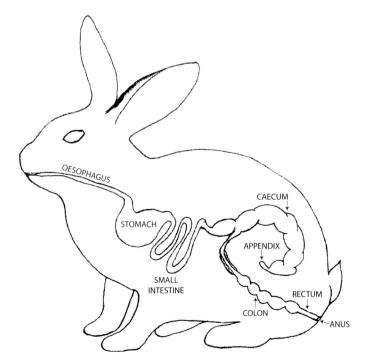

A rough diagram of the rabbit digestive system. This is not to scale.

Caecotrophs

Rabbits have a rather strange behaviour, which many owners may not even be aware of. From about 3 weeks of age they start to ingest faeces (droppings) straight from their bottom. This is perfectly normal and vitally essential. The act of eating faeces (known as coprophagy or caecotrophy) usually occurs at night, which is why they are often called night faeces. Night faeces or caecotrophs are droppings which are formed from fermentation of digestible fibre. Caecotrophs are rich in

nutrients including: vitamins, minerals, essential fatty acids and amino acids, which are only properly absorbed the second time through the digestive system.

Caecotrophs are usually soft sticky dark coloured droppings. They may have a green tinge to them and they are covered in a protective layer of mucus. However, the rabbit actually produced two types of dropping. The other type is not consumed and is a harder faecal pellet (containing indigestible fibre) which is deposited during the daylight hours around the hutch and the rest of their territory.

On average an adult rabbit will evacuate 360 hard pellets – total weight of about four ounces – above ground every twenty-four hours. Lockley (1965) [1]

The act of caecotrophy may have evolved to aid rabbits in environments where food was scarce. Another suggestion to why rabbits carry out caecotrophy is that when they are above ground they must eat as much grass as quickly as possible to avoid being caught by a predator. Once safely below ground they can ingest food (the caecotrophs) for a second time and digest the nutrients more slowly. Another evolutionary benefit is that food travels quickly through the rabbit's digestive system, so they don't have to escape predators whilst running with a full stomach!

Stress

Stress and pain have a negative effect on the digestive system of the rabbit. Caecotrophy only occurs in healthy rabbits and stress may alter normal caecotrophy production (Wilber 1999 [2]). Stress has also been identified as one cause for dysbiosis.

The Hay and Greens Diet

The recommended diet for a pet rabbit is known as the Hay and Greens Diet. This is a very high fibre diet. Unfortunately, many owners do not feed a diet such as this and use dry rabbit food (pellets or coarse/flaked mixes) as the bulk of the diet. These dry foods are often overfed or free fed causing many health problems.

1) The bulk of the diet should be grass or high quality grass hay. This should be freely available at all times.

2) Then the 'greens' which include vegetables, wild plants and herbs can be added. Green leafy vegetables should be fed every day with a selection of other cultivated vegetables, wild plants and herbs. Ideally 5-6 different 'greens' should be fed every day to give the rabbit a varied diet.

3) Dry pellets or coarse/flaked mixes for rabbits should only form a very small part of the diet and house rabbits, obese rabbits or rabbits that suffer from digestive problems may even suit a diet which contains no dry pellets or coarse mix at all.

4) Fruit and sugary items like carrots or fruit can be used occasionally as treats along with dry or fresh herbs.

Grass or hay should be the bulk of your rabbit's diet

The idea of giving your rabbit 5-6 different types of vegetables per day is to provide variety. Wild rabbits do not just eat grass – they eat a variety of grasses, weeds, flowering plants and crops! In the winter when food is scarce they will also resort to eating twigs and bark – in fact they can do considerable damage to young saplings. Rabbits lucky enough to have access to traditional hay meadows can come across many different species of flowering plants and grasses in just a few metres. The vegetables and greens you feed are designed to provide different nutrients, such as those a wild rabbit would come across.

Variety is also worth remembering when you select hay to feed your rabbits. Try and alternate the types of hay or feed meadow hay from traditionally managed, species-rich fields.

Nutrients

Originally commercial dry diets (pelleted or coarse/flaked foods) for rabbits were designed to make them grow rapidly and to a large size for their use as a meat source. Now there are many more diets suitable for pet rabbits and because of this their life span is increasing. The average life span is about 7-10 years [3] but some rabbits are now living on into their teens (this is especially true for rabbits which are neutered).

Protein
Proteins have several functions. For example enzymes are proteins, as are hormones. Protein is used for growth and tissue repair. Structural proteins can be found in cell walls, bone, muscle and connective tissues. Protein is also used as an energy source. More protein is needed by the rabbit during periods such as growth and reproduction.

If your rabbit does not get enough protein it could suffer problems such as poor growth, weight loss, poor coat condition, muscle wasting, anorexia and even death. Too much protein however can equally cause health problems.

Fat
Fats/oils have many functions. They are needed for heat, insulation, regulation of body temperature, regulation of hormone production, protection of vital organs (cushioning) and the production of fatty acids.

Carbohydrates
Carbohydrates are made from three elements: carbon, hydrogen and oxygen. Carbohydrates are used for energy, heat production and as components for the production of other nutrients. The most important carbohydrate is glucose, which is used as an energy source by the body. Diets high in carbohydrates are not suitable for rabbits, they may lead to obesity and digestive problems.

Fibre
Fibre is **very** important for rabbits. Experts believe that a diet for an adult rabbit should contain a **minimum** fibre level of 20-25% [4]. However, a rabbit's daily intake of fibre should be far higher than this. Dry pelleted foods or flaked mixes cannot be fed as a complete diet.

Types of hay

There are several types of hay and they can be separated in to two categories: Grass hay, which includes Timothy, meadow, oat and orchard hay (Cocksfoot) and legume hay, which includes alfalfa (lucerne) and clover. Grass hay is more suitable for adult rabbits than legume hay as it is generally higher in fibre but lower in calcium. Alfalfa and clover are higher in calcium and protein so long term feeding could aggravate urinary and kidney problems in adult rabbits. However, legume hay is suitable for young or breeding rabbits with higher energy requirements.

	Dry Matter %	Fibre %	Calcium %
Alfalfa Hay (sun cured) - early bloom*	89	24.9	1.33
Alfalfa Hay (sun cured) - full bloom*	88	30.6	1.13
Oat Hay (sun cured)**	91	27.8	0.22
Orchard Grass Hay (sun cured) - late bloom**	91	33.6	0.35
Timothy Hay (sun cured) - mid bloom*	88	30.0	0.36

*Figures from Nutrient Requirements of Rabbits, Second Revised Edition, 1977 Washington D.C. National Academy of Sciences.

** Figures from United States-Canadian Tables of Feed Composition, Third Revision, 1982, Washington D.C. National Academy of Sciences.

The nutrient levels in hay depend on when in the season it is cut. The early, mid and full bloom terms indicate how mature the plant was when it was harvested.

Meadow hay is not included in this chart. This is because it is hard to give an exact fibre and calcium figure as meadow hay is a collection of plants rather than one single species. In traditional hay meadows in the UK there can be over 30 species of plants per square metre including Sweet vernal, Crested Dog's Tail, Meadow Fox Tail, Meadow and Red Fescue, Cocksfoot, Lady's Bedstraw and Timothy. Meadow hay is an excellent source of fibre for rabbits and generally contains less calcium than Alfalfa hay.

Grass

Wild rabbits have a diet which almost exclusively consists of grass. Ideally a healthy rabbit would have daily access to plenty of fresh grass keeping it healthy, busy and your lawn mowed! Wilted lawn mower clippings and mouldy grass cuttings should not be fed. Neither should grass taken from the side of a road where traffic fumes are present or from a park where dogs and other animals may have urinated or defecated on it. If you have an indoor rabbit and it does not have access to a garden, you may wish to grow some grass (and wild plants) in trays or pots. Growing your grass in a large container such as plastic under-bed storage box will give your rabbit the opportunity to dig too. High quality hay is the next best thing to fresh grass.

Ensure that any grass, wild plants, hay and vegetables are free of insecticides and pesticides before offering them to your bunny.

Cold or frozen vegetables from the fridge should not be fed as they may cause diarrhoea and/or bloat. Frozen vegetables provide the perfect breeding ground for bacteria and other micro organisms as they begin to defrost and this may alter the balance of the friendly bacteria in the gut.

Grass wilts quickly and any uneaten grass should be collected and thrown away if not consumed within 10-15 minutes.

Grass is a high fibre, low fat diet

Dry Rabbit Food

It is possible with the correct balance of hay and vegetables to feed your rabbit successfully without the need for dry coarse/flaked mix or pellets food (Kelleher, 2003) [5]. A diet based on hay and vegetables with little or no dry food is generally recommended for adult indoor rabbits which need to lose weight or are having on-going digestive problems.

Unless you are willing to offer a variety of hay, vegetables, herbs and wild plants every day you should continue to feed small amounts of commercial dry rabbit food to ensure you rabbit gets everything it needs. Outdoor and growing rabbits may need more dry pellets/mix as they use more calories for growth and to keep warm in colder weather.

A pellet or mix food can be used as a supplement

If you do wish to supplement your rabbit's diet with a little dry food then try to:

Avoid diets with colourings. Several colourings have been banned from children's foods and are being excluded from dog/cat food because of concerns over their toxicity. Amongst other things it is thought that these colours may amplify behaviour problems.

Avoid letting your rabbit feed selectively (pick out their favourite bits). This may lead to deficiencies in some minerals. If your rabbit seems to pick at the coarse/flaked mix rabbit foods (the ones that look like muesli) try offering a pelleted food where the pieces are all the some (mono-component diet).

The diet on the left should avoid selective feeding

Avoid adult rabbit food which has fibre content lower than 18% (the higher the better according to many vets). High fibre diets are not as palatable as pellets with low fibre, high fat levels. Manufacturers of pet foods often want their dry food to be tasty so increasing the fibre content is not always in their best interest.

Avoid rabbit food with levels of protein higher than 12% (Kelly et al, 1996) [6] unless it is a young or breeding rabbit. Too much protein may lead to the over-production of caecotrophs. This is because high carbohydrate and high protein diets can change the rabbit's internal pH allowing the growth of harmful bacteria.

Avoid rabbit foods that contain more than 2-4% fat (Hand et al, 2000) [7] unless it is a young or breeding rabbit. Studies have found that foods that are higher in fat are tastier but are usually not healthier, especially if the rabbit is not physically active.

Avoid rabbit foods which contain high levels of calcium. The ideal level is around 0.5-0.6% (about 510mg) [8] for adult rabbits.

Avoid foods containing sugar or similar sweet products such as molasses, corn syrup, sugar beet and locust beans. These are used to make food more palatable, however may lead to dental decay, obesity and further problems. Some studies on children have linked sugar consumption with destructive, aggressive and restless behaviour. Similarly many dog trainers believe diet affects canine behaviour. Perhaps this is worth remembering when you notice an increase in rabbit activities like chewing furniture, nipping and digging!

Avoid diets containing nuts and seeds. These are high in fat and starch. Starch and sugar can increase the growth of harmful bacteria in the digestive system and lead to obesity.

Avoid feeding dry mix or pellets ad libitum (free feeding). This usually results in obesity and causes many rabbits to refuse high fibre hay and vegetables because they are too full. They may even stop practicing caecotrophy because they are not hungry. This can cause severe digestive and dental problems. Daily amounts of dry rabbit food should be carefully monitored.

Complete or complementary?

Commercial pet foods can be complementary or complete. A complete food has all the nutrients your pet needs and it can be fed on its own with no other foods, however dry pelleted or coarse rabbits foods are complementary as hay and fresh greens must be offered every day.

Probiotics and prebiotics

Probiotics are sometimes added to dry rabbit foods to aid the digestive systems. Probiotics are beneficial or 'friendly' bacteria, which are thought to promote digestion. They help to remove toxins from the gut, fight infections and produce an environment which is unfavourable for the growth of harmful bacteria. Speak to your vet about the most suitable probiotic as some types may not be appropriate. For example many human foods use *Lactobacilli* as the probiotic but more recent research suggests that the rabbit's digestive system actually contains high levels of *Bacteroides* bacteria.

Prebiotics feed the natural gut flora and consist of nutrients which promote growth of the friendly bacteria.

A healthy rabbit fed on the Hay and Greens diet should have no need for additional probiotics. However, rabbits prone to digestive problems or those on antibiotics may benefit from this type of dietary supplementation. Antibiotics can encourage the overgrowth of harmful bacteria.

Salt and mineral licks

Supplements should not be necessary if the rabbit is on a good quality diet, as most vitamins are properly absorbed the second time through the body (when the rabbit eats caecotrophs). Caecotrophs contain a large amount of B vitamins.

Vitamins

Most dry rabbit foods list Vitamins A, D and E on the bag. This is a legal requirement but many more vitamins will actually be included in the food.

Vitamin A (Retinol) is most commonly found in foods of animal origin i.e. meat and dairy. However vegetables such as carrots, spinach, pumpkin and watercress contain carotenes, e.g. beta-carotene, which can be changed in the body to vitamin A. This vitamin is essential for fighting infections and maintaining healthy eyes, bones and skin.

Vitamin E (Tocopherol). Vegetable oil, nuts and seeds are the richest sources of vitamin E but vegetables also contain small amounts especially broccoli, spinach and sprouts. Coccidiosis has been reported to increase the requirement for Vitamin E. This vitamin's main function in the body is as an antioxidant.

Vitamin D (Calciferol) is important for maintaining healthy bones and teeth.

Humans obtain vitamin D from sunlight. Vitamin D is produced when the bare skin is exposed to sunlight (specifically the wavelength known as UVB).

However, house rabbits do not receive exposure to sunlight (glass blocks UVB rays) and instead get all their vitamin D from the food they eat – including hay. Levels of vitamin D in hay depends on the variety of hay, whether it was sun or barn dried and how long the hay was sun dried for. Levels of vitamin D decrease over time so fresh hay will contain a larger amount.

However, studies show that although house rabbits are not deficient in Vitamin D they do have lower levels than rabbits housed outside and can suffer more spinal and dental problems [9].

So how do rabbits produce Vitamin D if their skin is covered in fur?

Researchers Carpenter and Zhao (1999) [10] state that birds and fur covered mammals such as rabbits ingest vitamin D when they groom themselves and this is supported by Downer (1999) [1]. Downer says that the large rabbit ears act as suntraps and that the natural oil on the surface of rabbit ears (which are covered with a much finer fur than the rest of the body) contains a chemical which when exposed to sunlight breaks down to form Vitamin D. The rabbit then ingests the vitamin D when licking its paws after grooming its ears.

Most dry foods are fortified with Vitamin D but this is certainly a factor to consider when deciding to keep your rabbits indoors or outdoors.

Some of the other vitamins found in fruit and vegetables

Vitamin B6 (Pyridoxine) is found in bananas and Brussel sprouts. Amongst other functions it is used in the formation of red blood cells and antibodies.

Vitamin C (Ascorbic acid) is found mainly in fruit and green leafy vegetables. It is an essential vitamin for the repair of skin and other body tissues. It helps the body resist infections, strengthens blood vessels and also helps with the formation of healthy bones and teeth. Rabbits can make their own vitamin C, humans and guinea pigs cannot make their own vitamin C and so a dietary source is essential.

Vitamin K, is found in many green leafy vegetables especially spinach and cauliflowers. Vitamin K is essential for normal blood clotting.

Folic Acid is found in leafy vegetables (like spinach and broccoli). A deficiency in this vitamin can cause anaemia as it is used in the production of red blood cells. It also helps the nervous system and acts to support normal growth and reproduction.

Antioxidants

Vitamins C, E and Beta-carotene are also known for their antioxidant properties. Antioxidants are molecules which help reduce damage to the body's cells by neutralising atoms called free radicals. Free radicals are produced during an essential process called oxidation. Free radicals can break down cell structures causing diseases such as cancer and ageing. Antioxidants are thought to slow or even prevent damage caused by free radicals, fruit and vegetables contain high levels of antioxidants which is why humans are advised to eat at least five portions a day.

Calcium

Calcium is a very important mineral in the rabbit's diet. Their delicate bones fracture easily and calcium may help to prevent this problem.

Rabbits can absorb calcium very efficiently. They are the only mammal that absorbs all the available dietary calcium rather than just the calcium that is required for normal body function. They excrete calcium via the urine instead of in bile (as in other animals): therefore excess dietary calcium may result in urinary crystals (mineral deposits that form in the bladder). An excess of calcium may also lead to calcification of the aorta and kidneys. If *Vitamin D* is taken in excess, this can exacerbate the effect of calcium.

Vegetables high in calcium include spinach, watercress, kale and parsley. Alfalfa hay is higher in calcium than grass hay such as timothy, oat or meadow.

© Cotton Tails Rabbit and Guinea Pig Rescue

Changing Diets

Any dietary change should be done gradually. A sudden change in diet (especially to a low fibre diet, high protein diet) causes a change in the pH of the gut. This increase in pH changes the balance of 'good and bad' bacteria in the digestive system (dysbiosis) allowing population increases in harmful bacteria such as *E-Coli* and *Clostridium spiriforme*. These bacteria release toxins that lead to serious health problems and death. Stress can also alter the balance of bacteria because stress reduces gut motility (it increases the time it takes for food to pass) allowing the bacteria time to proliferate.

In weaning rabbits (who are coming off their mother's milk) and young rabbits a very gradual introduction to pellets can help prevent conditions such as weaning enteritis and mucoid enteropathy [2]. Ensuring weaning and young rabbits have access to a high fibre diet (plenty of hay) is crucial and can help avoid these ailments occurring. Other factors which cause these conditions include stress such as being taken away from litter mates or leaving the pet shop or breeder to go to a new home [13].

If you are thinking of changing your adult rabbits diet from one brand of dry coarse/flaked or pelleted commercial food to another, this must also be done gradually over a few days. A sudden change in diet (especially if changing to a lower fibre diet) can result in enteritis [14]. To change diets, a little of the new food should be mixed with the current diet. As you increase the daily amount of the new brand of food the current food can be reduced and eventually weaned out completely.

Dry coarse/flaked or pelleted commercial rabbit food should never be suddenly cut out of the rabbit's diet. If you are considering this please speak to a veterinary surgeon about gradually weaning the food out.

Fruit and Vegetables

Feeding fruit

Although fruit contains important nutrients such as Vitamin C, feeding large amounts should be avoided. In the wild rabbits would have little access to fruit and this would not be a major part of their natural diet. As they are high in sugar feeding fruit and carrots in excess may lead to obesity and dental disease. Too much sugar and starch from fruit can also cause an overgrowth of harmful bacteria in the gut resulting in sticky bottom.

Fresh or dried herbs can be used as a healthy alternative to fruit. If fruit is fed it should be as a treat rather than part of the main diet. Try and limit fruit to one or two tablespoons per day and if possible offer fruits which are higher in fibre and lower in sugar.

Fruits to feed as a treat include: apple (not the seeds), apricot, blackberries and their leaves, blueberries, cherries, , kiwi, mango, melon, nectarines, orange segments (not the peel) peaches, pears, pineapple, plum, raspberries, raspberry leaves, strawberries and their leaves and tomatoes (not tomato leaves, these are poisonous). Although banana and grapes are non-toxic they contain very high sugar levels and should be avoided.

	Sugar (g)	Fibre (g)
Raspberry	4.6	2.5
Carrots	5.6	2.4
Pear	10	2.2
Kiwi	10.3	1.9
Apple	11.8	1.8
Orange	8.5	1.7
Strawberry	6	1.1
Banana	20.9	1.1
Grape	15.4	0.7

The information in this table denotes the grams of sugar and fibre in 100g of the fruit.
*Adapted from **The Composition of Foods** (Fifth edition). McCance and Widdowson (1991).*[15]

Vegetables

Suitable vegetables and plants include: asparagus, basil, broccoli, Brussel sprouts, cabbage, carrots and carrot tops, cauliflower and cauliflower leaves, celery and celery leaves, celeriac, chicory (and chicory relations including curly/ frisée endive, escarole and radicchio), clover, courgette, cucumber, dandelion leaves and flowers, dill, kale, marigold, mint leaves, parsley, parsnips, pea pods, peppers, plantain, radish tops, red cabbage, rocket, Romaine lettuce, spinach, spring greens, swede, Swiss chard (red and green) turnips and watercress.

As mentioned previously some vegetables and wild plants are higher in calcium than others e.g. watercress, parsley, dandelions and spinach. These foods should be fed in moderation but need not be excluded from the diet.

Lettuce

Lettuce is not actually poisonous to rabbits but it does have a higher water content (as do cucumber, tomato and celery) and a lower fibre content than many vegetables which may be why it seems to give some rabbits an upset stomach. It also contains fewer minerals than other vegetables and a rabbit fed solely on lettuce would get little in the way of nutrition. For example in comparison spring greens contain more calcium, magnesium, iron and protein than lettuce.

	water	fibre
Spring greens	86.2	3.4
cabbage	90.1	2.4
tomatoes	91.2	1
celery	95.1	1.1
cucumber	96.4	0.6
lettuce	95.1	0.9
Iceberg lettuce	95.6	0.6

The information in this table denotes the grams of water and fibre in 100g of the vegetable. Adapted from The Composition of Foods (Fifth edition). McCance and Widdowson (1991) [15].

There are numerous types of lettuce but most fall into one of the following categories:

Romaine (Cos) Lettuce – e.g. Little Gem lettuce

Crisphead lettuce e.g. Iceberg lettuce

Loose leaf lettuce – e.g. Oak Leaf lettuce (Green/Red leaf), Lamb's lettuce, Lollo Rosso

Round lettuce (Butterhead lettuce) – e.g Boston lettuce, Bibb lettuce

As a general rule a little lettuce in the diet should not cause a problem however you should avoid Iceberg and the lighter leaf varieties and aim to feed the dark leafy types of lettuce instead.

Broccoli, cauliflower, cabbage, asparagus and Brussel sprouts contain a type of sugar called raffinose which is difficult to digest and in humans this has been linked to gas formation and bloating However, cabbage and spring greens can usually form a large part of your rabbits diet without any ill-effects as long as you start by offering small amounts and increase the quantity slowly. The other vegetables should be fed in moderation.

Sweet corn should not be fed to rabbits as it can cause a blockage and the high starch content can be difficult to digest and fattening. Baby sweet corn in small quantities may be suitable for some rabbits. As with all vegetables it is advisable to try small amounts only when introducing a new vegetable for the first time.

Onions, leeks and chives are all part of the same family of bulb plants known as Allium. They are toxic to rabbits and should be avoided.

Treats

Rabbits will eat chocolate, cakes, crackers and crisps if you let them, but these may lead to serious health problems, such as obesity, dental disease and digestive upset. Herbs such as dill, mint, basil, sage and coriander or some fruit plant leaves such as strawberry, raspberry or apple leaves can make a nice treat. Avoid leaves such as plum, peach, rhubarb and tomato leaves which can be poisonous

Tasty herbs and fruit may be used (under guidance from your vet) as a way of encouraging an anorexic rabbit or a rabbit which has just had surgery to start eating again. Dandelions are also useful as an appetite stimulant.

Poisonous plants

Rabbits cannot always distinguish between a safe plant and a poisonous one. If you are unsure whether something is safe to feed, don't feed it!

Plants to avoid include: bluebell, buttercup, deadly nightshade, dock (when in seed), evergreen tree and shrub foliage, honeysuckle, ivy, oak, peach leaves, plum leaves [16] poppy, potatoes, rhubarb and all plants from bulbs e.g. tulips, snowdrops and daffodils.

Water

Fresh water should always be available. Remember to check how much your rabbit drinks. If the amount changes dramatically, this can indicate a sign of ill health. A rabbit fed on fresh green food will drink less than a rabbit on a dry diet. A rabbit will drink on average 100ml of water per kg of body weight (Beynon et al, 1991) [17] each day.

Some rabbits may prefer to drink out of bowls rather than water bottles. In a recent study Tschudin et al (2011) [18] indicated that rabbits preferred drinking from open dishes and this allowed a faster water intake. Always offer your rabbit a choice of water sources. Bowls and bottles at different areas and heights should be available. Water bottles are more hygienic as bowls can be easily tipped over and if the rabbit dribbles water down its neck it can cause a problem called 'green fur' which is a type of dermatitis around the dewlap. Warm water can often encourage a rabbit to drink when it is poorly e.g. when recovering from surgery.

Common Health Problems

Sticky Bottom

Low fibre, high protein and high carbohydrate diets can cause the rabbit to create too many caecotrophs. The caecotrophs produced by these rabbits also appear softer and can stick to the fur around their bottom. This is known as 'sticky bottom'. If the rabbit fails to clean this waste the moist soiled fur attracts flies and other parasites. Sticky bottom may occur if the rabbit is overweight (it may be too fat to clean itself) or it may be too painful to clean the caecotrophs away due to arthritis or dental disease.

Rabbits which have a sticky bottom will produce soft sticky caecotrophs at night but they will still be leaving hard droppings during the day. If both the caecotrophs and the hard droppings are loose this is known as true diarrhoea. This is very serious and veterinary attention should be sought immediately.

Myasis (fly strike)

Fly strike usually occurs in the spring and summer when the weather is warm. Flies are attracted to the soiled fur around the rabbit's bottom. This fur may be soiled with urine or there could be a build up of sticky caecotrophs (Sticky Bottom Syndrome).

The flies lay their eggs in the soiled fur and with the right conditions these eggs can develop into maggots within 24 hours. So your rabbit should be checked daily. The maggots will look for open wounds but they will also eat intact skin, they then eat the flesh of the rabbit. In many cases euthanasia is often the only and kindest option. The maggots also produce a toxin which sends the rabbit into shock. Even if the damage to the flesh can heal the shock can be fatal.

If fly strike is suspected the rabbit should be taken to a vet immediately.

If your rabbit frequently suffers from a sticky bottom you should clean the area daily (usually warm soapy water is suitable) but avoid soaking the rabbit completely as moist fur is attractive to the flies. The fur should be thoroughly dried after washing. You may also be able to carefully cut out badly soiled fur. Even daily inspections may not be enough to ensure you catch this condition early as the eggs can hatch into maggots quickly. In the summer months you may also consider using products such as Rearguard produced by Novartis Animal Health, Rearguard contains the active ingredient Cyromazine which is an insect growth regulator. When this product is applied to the rabbit it stops the eggs from developing into maggots.

However, a change in diet to prevent a sticky bottom occurring again is essential. The rabbit's diet should be high in fibre and low in protein and carbohydrates. This means that high quality, high fibre hay and fresh greens should be offered with limited amounts of dry coarse/flaked or pelleted food. The Hay and Greens Diet is recommended. Occasionally you may hear people say that feeding fresh greens and vegetables causes a sticky bottom. This can be an issue if you feed too many fruit or sugary items like carrots or if you are feeding vegetables which are not fresh and have started to wilt.

To prevent flystrike the hutch should be kept scrupulously clean and you should seek veterinary help if your rabbit is not eating caecotrophs on a daily basis.

Your rabbit may also have these issues if he/she cannot reach to clean his/her bottom. This may be caused by obesity or arthritis which is discussed later in this book.

And finally, a worm infestation may cause sticky bottom but again this can be prevented easily. Treatments such as Panacur, an oral paste, are available through veterinary practices and pet shops.

© Cotton Tails Rabbit and Guinea Pig Rescue

Obesity

We have all seen the television programmes and read the reports on the increase of obesity in children and adults, but you may not know that the RSPCA estimates that 50% of all cats and dogs in the UK are overweight too. As rabbits are now the third most popular pet in the UK we also need to prevent rabbits getting too fat. Statistics show many pet rabbits are becoming obese. In 2007 Simon Wheeler from the PetPlan Insurance company said that dietary and obesity related illnesses made up 25% of all claims for rabbits [19].

Sugary/starchy treats and low fibre foods (such as crackers and biscuits) and a lack of exercise can lead to obesity.

An overweight rabbit will often suffer more health problems and will usually have a shorter lifespan. It may not be able to move around as efficiently, may not be able to reach its bottom to ingest caecotrophs and clean itself. This in turn could lead to a sticky bottom and an increased chance of fly strike. Extra weight may also put pressure on the bones causing arthritis as the rabbit gets older. Being overweight will also put strain on your rabbit's heart. You should be able to feel the ribs on a healthy rabbit.

Obesity and excess folds of skin around the bottom can lead to urine scald (scalding of the rear end and feet due to excess exposure to urine). This is common in overweight rabbits or rabbits kept in a hutch all day as they do not move around as much. Overweight rabbits may also suffer with sore hocks. Pressure is put on the feet and skin lesions (pododermatitis) can develop.

Bear in mind that an indoor rabbit may need less food than a rabbit kept outdoors in a hutch. This is because a rabbit kept inside does not need to generate as much energy to keep warm. This may also be the case with rabbits in the summer. As the weather gets warmer the rabbit will probably use less energy maintaining its body temperature.

Exercise and brittle bones

Osteoporosis has been linked to a lack of exercise so provide toys and play with your rabbit to persuade him/her to move. Many rabbits enjoy throwing toilet tubes and pine cones around, digging in old towels and ripping up newspapers or phone books Upturned boxes and tubes for hiding in are used to mimic their burrows and can provide fun, security and will encourage your rabbit to explore.

It is strongly recommended that rabbits are kept in pairs. In fact many rescue centres will not re-home single rabbits. Two rabbits are likely to more active by playing with each other.

Encourage exercise by hiding food around the rabbit's run or play area or even use feeding balls/toys designed for dogs and cats. Hide the food in toilet tubes (stuffing hay in toilet tubes is a good idea), scatter the food over the ground, hang the food from the roof of the cage/hutch or outdoor run, hide it in hay or under crumpled sheets of newspaper. Rabbits do not have particularly good eyesight but their sense of smell is good. Hopefully, this will encourage the rabbit to forage for a tasty treat (this is a great boredom buster too). This constant movement can help to burn off excess calories and prevent the rabbit from becoming overweight. When eating from a bowl the rabbit will usually sit in the same position until all the food is gone.

To properly enrich your rabbit's environment and prevent boredom try providing their living area with objects at different levels. Ramps, shelves, crates and boxes can all make exploring more fun. Jumping off slightly higher objects can help keep your rabbit active and mobile, as exercise will strengthen the bones and muscles.

Rapid weight loss is not recommended as it is dangerous. An overweight rabbit should ideally have its dry pelleted or coarse/flaked food cut down gradually until it can eventually be weaned out completely. As long as your rabbit has hay 24 hours a day and a variety of mixed greens every day then a dry food is not always necessary. Remember to use herbs and foods such as dandelion leaves as treats instead of crisps, biscuits and too much fruit.

Urinary Problems

Red urine
Rabbit urine varies between different shades of white, cloudy brown, orange, red and even clear colours. These can all be perfectly normal. For example, red urine can be a result of eating various plant materials such as dandelions and cabbage. It can also be caused by certain medications. However, it may indicate that blood is present in the urine (haematuria).

Sludgy urine
Thick, white creamy urine indicates a dietary problem. A diet which contains too much calcium or protein may cause the urine to be 'sludgy'. The urine may dry on the cage/hutch floor as a white mark. This colouration can also indicate that your rabbit has urinary crystals. Urinary crystals are collections of minerals formed together from excess amounts of calcium (for example) in the urine.

Symptoms of a urinary problem
Symptoms of cystitis and urinary crystals include blood in the urine, sitting in a hunched position, reluctance to move, teeth grinding, pain when urinating, weight loss, anorexia, loss of house training and frequent attempts to urinate. Cystitis is more common in female rabbits.

Using a high fibre, low protein, moderate calcium diet should prevent urinary conditions. Avoid feeding legume hay and stick to grass hay which has lower levels of calcium. Gradually reduce dry commercial rabbit food and replace this with hay, fresh or dry herbs, wild plants and vegetables.

Pododermatitis

This condition can be described as dermatitis of the feet or 'sore hocks'. The bottoms of the feet (which have no footpads) are covered in ulcers and scabs, the feet weep with a liquid which has a strong odour. Some owners may not notice pododermatitis if the rabbit is not handled frequently. This condition is often seen in young rabbits housed in unsuitable hutches/cages i.e. with wire floors. Overweight rabbits are at risk because of the excess pressure on the feet and because they are unlikely to be as active. This can be a very serious condition especially if the feet are abscessed. Abscesses may go to the bone and will need to be surgically removed and in some cases the whole foot may need to be amputated.

Fur Balls

Fur balls in rabbits are also known as trichobezoars. They are caused by a build up of hair/fur in the digestive system as rabbits can swallow fur accidentally when they are grooming themselves or their companion. When cats suffer from fur balls they can vomit to eliminate this blockage. Rabbits do not have the ability to vomit but a diet high in indigestible fibre will help to push the fur through the digestive system safely. Stress and boredom can cause over-grooming in rabbits so environmental enrichment may help prevent this problem.

If you rabbit has ingested a large amount of fur you may see your rabbit produce droppings resembling a 'string of pearls', where the droppings are joined by hair. String of pearls droppings are generally more common in long haired rabbits however it may also be seen in other breeds. It can be seen mainly in the months when the rabbit is moulting and ingesting more fur than usual. Brushing your rabbit and removing excess fur can help.

Dental Disease

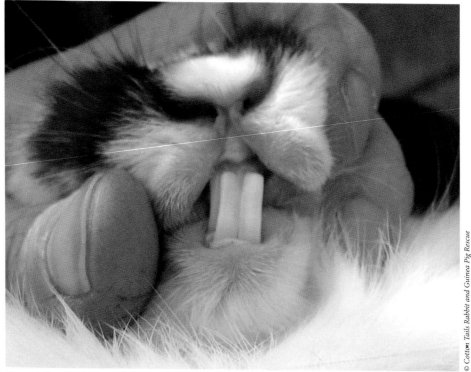

© Cotton Tails Rabbit and Guinea Pig Rescue

Dental disease is one of the most common problems that veterinary surgeons encounter in rabbits. In a survey of 102 rabbits as many as thirty rabbits were found to suffering from dental disease (Mullan & Main 2006) [20].

Rabbits are herbivores that have evolved to eat a diet which is high in fibre. Their teeth grow continuously in order to compensate for the wear and tear from long periods of chewing on touch fibrous material like grass and hay.

Dental disease can occur in both the incisors and cheek teeth. The top of the tooth is called the crown and the bottom is the root. Both the crown and the root can over grow and cause problems. If left unchecked the teeth can grow through the cheeks and head causing abscesses and even death.

The signs of dental disease

One of the first signs of dental disease is weight loss. Your rabbit may attempt to pick up food but dropping it again without chewing. Excessive drooling is also a symptom. If the chin, dewlap and chest become wet then bacterial infections, skin complaints and fur loss can occur. As well as drooling the owner may see signs of discharge from the eyes. This can lead to eye infections.

Rabbits do not show pain in the same way as other animals and a rabbit with dental pain may sit in a hunched position and grind its teeth. Mouth breathing indicates a serious problem as rabbits usually breathe through their nose.

Dental disease may also lead to skin and coat problems as the rabbit finds it too painful to groom itself. Digestive problems can also occur through selective feeding and because it is too painful to eat caecotrophs.

Causes of dental disease

A calcium or Vitamin D deficiency can occur if a rabbit is fed on a coarse mixed dry food and feeds selectively by picking only their favourite pieces. Deficiencies in these minerals and vitamins can cause dental disease. Selective feeding is also a sign that dental disease is already a problem. Rabbits with pain will select soft food like fruit but avoid hard dried diets and hay which needs grinding. A lack of fibre in the form of hay and vegetables may then lead to digestive problems including sticky bottom.

In some breeds dental problems can be caused by an inherited condition. The dwarf breeds and lop eared rabbits may be predisposed to dental problems due to the shape of their skull. The only way to prevent this is for breeders to only breed from rabbits with normal jaw anatomy.

However, in most cases diet is the most common cause of dental disease. Dry coarse/flaked or pelleted commercial rabbit food comes in relatively small concentrated amounts and is often very quickly. Hay and grass take longer to eat and this wears the teeth down. Grass and hay promote a grinding, chewing motion by the teeth but dried pelleted and flaked food is crushed and swallowed. This does not wear the teeth down in the same way.

The high fibre, hay and greens diet (explained at the start of this book) which involves offering high quality hay available 24 hours a day, fresh vegetables, wild plants with little or no dry coarse/flaked or pelleted commercial food can help prevent dental disease. Wood from fruit trees e.g. apple can be offered as an item for gnawing on.

Gastro-Intestinal Stasis

Gastrointestinal stasis occurs when there is no movement of food through the digestive system. This can be very uncomfortable for the rabbit and it may cause anorexia. If the rabbit stops eating this exacerbates the problem as there is no food (fibre) available to encourage movement through the digestive system.

Symptoms of GI stasis include smaller or unusual shaped droppings or even no drippings at all. The rabbit may be lethargic and showing signs of pain including sitting in a hunched position or grinding its teeth.

The most common cause of GI is a lack of dietary fibre, however other factors that influence this problem are:

> Stress
>
> Dehydration
>
> Bloat (gas)
>
> Dental problems (anorexia because it is too painful to eat)
>
> Blockages (such as hairballs)
>
> Urinary problems
>
> Lack of exercise

Bloat

Bloat occurs when the stomach fills up with gas. It is very serious and often fatal. You may see your rabbit adopting a hunched position, reluctance to move, eat or go to the toilet. The stomach will be swollen and any droppings passed will usually be much smaller than normal. Gas is produced from the fermentation of undigested food that has stopped moving through the digestive system.

Bloat is usually seen in rabbits on a low fibre, high carbohydrate and high protein diet. Although, feeding frozen vegetables and plants may also cause bloat.

 But it can also be caused by a hairball blockage, stress or a parasite infection. For example rabbits suffering from coccidiosis may have a bloated distended stomach and this condition is a result of an infection of the protozoan species *Eimeria*. Although some rabbit foods contain a medication (a coccidiostat) to aid the prevention of coccidiosis good hygiene is essential to prevent this disease.

Anorexia

If your rabbit has not eaten for more than 12 hours it is vital you seek veterinary attention immediately.

Anorexia is the term used to describe a lack of appetite. If your rabbit stops eating (becomes anorexic) then it is usually due to pain or stress. Anorexia is not a disease but a symptom of many conditions. If your rabbit stops eating the cause of anorexia must be rapidly determined by a veterinary surgeon. Rabbits which do not eat can quickly develop a condition called hepatic lipidosis (fatty liver disease) which can be fatal.

Your vet may ask you to encourage eating by hand-feeding tasty items such as dandelion leaves, herbs and fresh greens.

Glossary of digestive terms

Abscess – an area of inflammation with a collection of pus.

Ad lib – when relating to food it means that the food is offered freely and the amount is not restricted.

Anaesthetic – a drug which is used to sedate the rabbit so there is a loss of sensation during medical procedures.

Anorexia – lack of appetite (rabbit stops eating).

Arthritis – inflammation of a joint, usually characterised by pain and stiffness.

Bacteria – a small microscopic organism which can be beneficial or disease causing.

Caecotrophs – the first set of faeces produced by a rabbit. They are soft and smelly and are usually eaten.

Calcification – calcium builds up in the artery causing it to harden.

Coarse or flaked mix – a feed consisting of different coloured dried food pieces.

Coccidiosis – a parasitic disease.

Cystitis – inflammation of the bladder.

Dermatitis – inflammation of the skin (a skin infection).

Dewlap – a fold of skin found under the chin of female rabbits.

Digestive system – a group of organs which are involved in the eating, breaking down and absorption of food.

Enteritis – inflammation of the small intestine.

Environmental enrichment – the toys, games and activities used to prevent boredom and keep rabbit happy and active.

Enzymes – enzymes are proteins used as a catalyst which means they help speed up reactions in the body.

Euthanasia – the rabbit may need to be humanely killed or 'put to sleep' because it is too ill to recover.

Faeces – waste matter, also known as droppings, stools, excrement or poo.

Fermentation – this is a turbulent chemical reaction which changes one substance into another.

Fibrous – a tough material high in fibres.

Foliage – leaves of trees and plants.

Forage – to search for food.

Gastrointestinal – relating to the stomach and the intestines (digestive tract).

Genetic – the characteristic was passed on (inherited) from the parents.

Herbivores – animals that eat plants only (no insects or other animals).

Hocks – the ankle of a rabbit.

Hormones – a chemical made by the body which is used for controlling and regulating body functions e.g. reproductive behaviour.

Incisors – the sharp teeth at the front of the mouth, used for cutting.

Ingest – to eat, consume.

Intestinal flora - the term given to bacteria and micro-organisms in the gut.

Lesions – a wound or infected area on the skin.

Mammal – mammals are animals characterised by their warm blood, hair or fur and mammary glands.

Micro-organisms – organisms (like bacteria and germs) which can only be seen through a microscope.

Mucoid enteropathy – an intestinal disease in which large amounts of mucus is found in the colon. There is also often a blockage in the caecum. Droppings may be coated in mucus.

Obesity – very overweight, usually 20-30% more than the ideal weight should be.

Osteoporosis – weak, brittle bones which are very porous and have reduced protein and calcium levels.

Over-grooming – excessive licking, biting, chewing and sucking of the fur.

pH – this is a measurement of acidity or alkalinity. Some bacteria like to grow an acidic environment, others prefer an alkaline environment.

Predator – an animal that hunts and eats other animals to survive.

Prey – an animal that is hunted and eaten as a source of food for other animals.

Scald – a burn caused by exposure to liquid.

Sedative – something that has a calming effect reduces anxiety and stress.

Soiled – soiling around the rabbit's bottom occurs when the fur is stained or coated in urines and/or faeces.

Stasis – the normal movement of food through the digestive system has stopped.

Sticky bottom – sticky droppings which are stuck to the fur around the anus.

Urine – a liquid containing waste products (also called pee or wee!).

References

1 Lockley, R.M. (1980). *The Private Life of the Rabbit*, published by London, Book Club Associates.

2 Wilber, J. L. (1999). *Pathology of the Rabbit*, published by Washington D C Department of Veterinary Pathology. Armed Forces Institute of Pathology.

3 The Rabbit Welfare Association and Fund website www.rabbitwelfare.co.uk

4 Rosenthal, K. L. (2005). *Basic Rabbit Medicine and Husbandry*, BSAVA Congress Scientific Proceedings, 48th Annual Congress p357. Flecknell, P. (2000) *BSAVA Manual of Rabbit Medicine and Surgery*, Gloucester p21.

5 Kelleher, S. A. (2003). *Dealing with G I Problems*. BSAVA Congress Scientific Proceedings, 46th Annual Congress. Meredith, A. *The Importance of Diet in Rabbits*, British Rabbit Council funded paper.

6 Kelly, Noel, C. & Wills, J. M. (1996). *Manual of Companion Animal Nutrition and Feeding*. Cheltenham, BSAVA, p218.

7 Hand et al (2000), *Small Animal Clinical Nutrition*. 4th edition, Kansas USA. Mark Morris Institute.

8 Kelly, Noel, C. & Wills, J. M. (1996). *Manual of Companion Animal Nutrition and Feeding*. Cheltenham, BSAVA, p270. Wilsbach, K. *Lowering Blood Calcium*, The House Rabbit Society website. King, C. *Calcium problems in rabbits*, The Rabbit Welfare Association and Fund website.

9 Saunders, R. Rabbits: *Environment and Disease*. The Rabbit Welfare Association and Fund website.

10 Carpenter, K. J. and Zhao, L. (1999). *Forgotten mysteries in the early history of Vitamin D*. The Journal of Nutrition, 129, 923 – 927.

11 Downer, J. (1999). *Supernatural. The unseen powers of animals*. London, BBC Worldwide Ltd, p56.

12 Richardson, V. (2000). *Rabbits: Health, Husbandry and Diseases*. Oxford, Blackwell Science.

13 Meredith, A. (2005). *The Importance of Diet in Rabbits*. British Rabbit Council funded paper.

14 Richardson, V. (2000). *Rabbits: Health, Husbandry and Diseases*. Oxford, Blackwell Science.

15 Food Standards Agency (2002). *The Composition of Food*, McCance and Widdowson, sixth summary edition. Cambridge, Royal Society of Chemistry.

16 James, C. (1997). *The Really Useful Bunny Guide*, Carolina James. Kingdom Books.

17 Beynon, P. H. & Cooper, J. E. (1991). BSAVA Manual of Exotic Pets. Cheltenham, BSAVA, p73.

18 Tschudin, A., Clauss, M., Codron, D., Hatt, J. M. (2011). Preference of rabbits for drinking from open dishes versus nipple drinkers. Veterinary Record, 168 (7): 190-190a.

19 The Telegraph, 18 November 2007. Sweet Treats Creating Wave of Tubby Bunnies. http://www.telegraph.co.uk/news/uknews/1569691/Sweet-treats-creating-wave-of-tubs-bunnies.html

20 Mullan, S. M., Main, D. C. J. (2006). Survey of the husbandry, health and welfare of 102 pet rabbits. Veterinary record. Volume 159: 103 – 109.

ACKNOWLEDGEMENTS

Thank you to the Rabbit Welfare Association and Fund and Cotton Tails Rabbit and Guinea Pig Rescue for help with photographs.

Also thanks to Rowan Flindall for all her help and Owen Davies MRCVS for veterinary input.

RECOMMENDED READING

House Rabbit Handbook. How to Live with an Urban Rabbit by Marinell Harriman. Drollery Press 4th Edition (2005)

Greenfoods for Rabbits and Cavies by F.R. Bell. Coney Publications (Available through Fur & Feather magazine, www.furandfeather.co.uk, 01473 652789)

Rabbit Nutrition by Virginia Richardson MRCVS. Coney Publications (Available through Fur & Feather magazine, www.furandfeather.co.uk, 01473 652789)

USEFUL WEBSITES

Rabbit Welfare Association & Fund www.rabbitwelfare.co.uk

House Rabbit Society www.rabbit.org

Rabbits United Forum http://forums.rabbitrehome.org.uk

Burns Pet Nutrition Ltd (producer of traditionally grown meadow hay) www.burnspet.co.uk